# Glencoe Science

# Critical Thinking/ Problem Solving

## Earth Science

## Glencoe McGraw-Hill

New York, New York    Columbus, Ohio    Woodland Hills, California    Peoria, Illinois

# Glencoe Science

Student Edition
Teacher Wraparound Edition
Interactive Teacher Edition CD-ROM
Interactive Lesson Planner CD-ROM
Lesson Plans
Content Outline for Teaching
Dinah Zike's Teaching Science with Foldables
Directed Reading for Content Mastery
Foldables: Reading and Study Skills
Assessment
   Chapter Review
   Chapter Tests
   ExamView Pro Test Bank Software
   Assessment Transparencies
   Performance Assessment in the Science
     Classroom
   The Princeton Review Standardized Test
     Practice Booklet
Directed Reading for Content Mastery in Spanish
Spanish Resources
English/Spanish Guided Reading Audio Program

Reinforcement
Enrichment
Activity Worksheets
Section Focus Transparencies
Teaching Transparencies
Laboratory Activities
Science Inquiry Labs
Critical Thinking/Problem Solving
Reading and Writing Skill Activities
Mathematics Skill Activities
Cultural Diversity
Laboratory Management and Safety in the Science
   Classroom
MindJogger Videoquizzes and Teacher Guide
Interactive Explorations and Quizzes CD-ROM
Vocabulary Puzzlemaker Software
Cooperative Learning in the Science Classroom
Environmental Issues in the Science Classroom
Home and Community Involvement
Using the Internet in the Science Classroom

## To the Teacher

Critical Thinking/Problem Solving worksheets in this booklet exercise the students' abilities to apply thinking skills to situations related to concepts presented in the student edition. Students will apply their knowledge to a new situation, analyze the new information, and synthesize in order to respond in a creative way. A series of responses that students might give are provided for you at the end of this booklet.

## Glencoe/McGraw-Hill

A Division of The **McGraw·Hill** Companies

Send all inquiries to:
Glencoe/McGraw-Hill
8787 Orion Place
Columbus, OH 43240

ISBN 0-07-825411-6
Printed in the United States of America
9 10 009 06 05

# Table of Contents

# Critical Thinking / Problem Solving Skills Correlation

| Skill | Activity | | | | | | | | | | | | | | | | | | | | | | |
|---|---|---|---|---|---|---|---|---|---|---|---|---|---|---|---|---|---|---|---|---|---|---|---|
| | 1 | 2 | 3 | 4 | 5 | 6 | 7 | 8 | 9 | 10 | 11 | 12 | 13 | 14 | 15 | 16 | 17 | 18 | 19 | 20 | 21 | 22 | 23 |
| Clarifying issues | | | | | | | | | | | | | | | ✔ | | | | ✔ | | | | |
| Comparing and contrasting | | | | | ✔ | | ✔ | | | ✔ | | | | | | | | | | ✔ | ✔ | | ✔ |
| Developing a perspective | | ✔ | | | | | | | ✔ | | | | | | | | | ✔ | ✔ | | | | |
| Distinguishing relevant from irrelevant facts | ✔ | | | | | | | | | | | | | | | ✔ | | | | | | | |
| Drawing conclusions | ✔ | ✔ | | | | | | ✔ | | | | | | | | ✔ | | | ✔ | | | | ✔ |
| Evaluating information | | | | ✔ | ✔ | | | | | ✔ | | ✔ | | | | | | ✔ | | | | | |
| Examining and evaluating assumptions | | | | | | | | | | | | | ✔ | | | | | | | | | | |
| Extrapolating data/information | | | | | | ✔ | | ✔ | | | ✔ | | | ✔ | | | | | | | | | |
| Generating and assessing solutions | | | | | | | | ✔ | | | | | ✔ | | | | | | | ✔ | | ✔ | |
| Making a hypothesis | | | | | | | | | | | | | | ✔ | ✔ | | | | | | | | |
| Making predictions or interpretations | | | ✔ | | ✔ | | ✔ | | ✔ | | ✔ | | | | | | | | | | | | |
| Making judgments | | | ✔ | | | | ✔ | ✔ | ✔ | | | | | | | | | | | | | | |
| Observing and inferring | | | | | | | | | | | | | | | | | ✔ | | ✔ | | | | |
| Recognizing cause and effect | ✔ | | | | | | | | | | | | | | | | ✔ | | | | ✔ | ✔ | |
| Summarizing/synthesizing | | | | | | | | | | | ✔ | ✔ | | | | | | | | | | | |
| Classifying | | | | ✔ | | | | | | | | | | | | | | | | | | | |

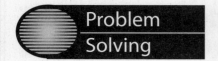 Problem Solving

# Earth's Last Frontier— Hydrothermal Vents

In 1977, scientists found something so unusual and so hard to get to, it's a wonder they ever made the discovery. Three scientists, diving in a small research submarine 2,348 m deep in the Pacific Ocean, discovered the first hydrothermal vent.

Hydrothermal vents are geysers in the ocean floor. They are created when ocean water seeps into Earth's crust through cracks on the seafloor. The ocean water, heated by magma and hot rocks, spews out, carrying minerals from inside Earth.

### Forming Chimneys

When the hot water (380°C or more) mixes with the cold seawater (2°C), it cools quickly. The minerals in the water settle and gradually form deposits that create a chimney at the opening of the vent. Because the chimneys spew hot, mineral-rich water, they can look like they're smoking. The diameter of the openings on the vents can be as small as a few centimeters or as large as several meters. Scientists discovered one vent that was as tall as a 16-story building and at least 183 m across.

Hydrothermal vents are found in all the oceans, but most are along an area of active volcanoes known as the Mid-Ocean Ridge. They form where ocean plates have separated, allowing lava to flow through. To find a vent, scientists look for increased seawater temperatures or volcanic activity.

### Ocean Floor Biocommunities

Until hydrothermal vents were discovered, most scientists thought organisms could not survive at such great depths because of extreme pressure, absence of sunlight, and low temperatures. Scientists were surprised to find that many hydrothermal vents had thriving biocommunities around them. Giant tube worms and blind shrimp are just some of the more than 300 species found near the vents.

What is at the base of the food chain that supports these deep-sea animals? After analyzing the water, scientists discovered it is a type of bacteria. This special bacteria can convert the toxic sulfur from the vents into energy. This process of using chemicals rather than sunlight for energy is called chemosynthesis. In turn, other vent organisms eat these bacteria or they eat other organisms that eat the bacteria.

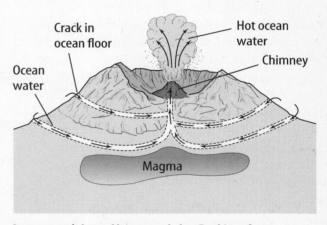

Ocean water is heated by magma below Earth's surface.

### A New Frontier

The extreme depths make it difficult to locate and study hydrothermal vents, and the special equipment required is expensive. Scientists have explored less than one percent of the seafloor where they think vents might be located.

Scientists do know that geothermal vents play an important role in heating the world's oceans and maintaining their chemical balance. They also serve as an outlet for the heat within Earth's crust. In the future, these unique ecosystems might prove to be sources for new medicines and might even be mined for their copper, gold, and manganese they emit.

## Applying Problem Solving Skills

1. If you had been able to interview one of the scientists who discovered the first hydrothermal vents, what questions would you have asked? List at least three.

2. Why was the discovery of the sulfur-eating bacteria important to scientists' understanding of this unique ocean-floor ecosystem?

3. Why do you think hydrothermal vents are called "Earth's last frontier"?

## Critical Thinking

# Atomic Energy—Good and Bad

**Activity 2**

The majority of chemical elements never change. An element might combine with other elements to form compounds, but the structure of the atoms in each element remains the same. Such elements are stable. Some elements, in contrast, are not stable. They change over time, becoming different elements. As these elements change, they release energy. The energy they release is called radiation, so the elements are radioactive.

Once scientists understood the nature of radioactive elements, they realized that all atoms store a great deal of energy. Scientists found that splitting atoms releases energy in the form of heat and radiation. Splitting atoms is known as fission. Fission happens when the atoms of radioactive elements are bombarded with neutrons. The neutrons penetrate the nucleus of the atom and cause the atoms to divide in half. This splitting causes the release of tremendous amounts of energy, which can be harnessed.

### Uses of Nuclear Energy

The first use of atomic energy was in warfare. Atomic bombs were made that split atoms upon impact, producing waves of searing heat and deadly levels of radiation. When the United States dropped fission bombs on Japan during World War II, hundreds of thousands of people were killed and much land was destroyed. Later, scientists learned to harness atomic energy for peaceful means, such as generating electricity.

After the war, nuclear reactors were built throughout the world. In a nuclear reactor, atoms of radioactive elements are split. Some of the energy released is in the form of heat. The heat is used to produce steam, which powers turbines that create electricity and provide power to cities and factories.

In a nuclear reactor, the heat must be controlled. If too much heat builds up, it causes an explosion that releases radioactive elements into the air. The radioactive elements do not disappear. They are absorbed by other elements and can increase. Too much radiation is harmful to people, animals, and plants. It can cause sickness and even death.

### Chornobyl and Beyond

Because radiation is so harmful to living things, great care has been taken to create safety procedures to prevent accidents. But in 1986, an accident did happen. In Chornobyl, Ukraine, part of the former Soviet Union, a steam buildup resulted in an explosion that released large amounts of radiation into the atmosphere. The explosion devastated the area around the reactor and caused 31 deaths. The radiation, blown by wind, was detected in places far away from Chornobyl.

Years later, the physical and psychological effects of the accident are still evident. There is a significant increase in thyroid cancer, especially among children. Anxiety and stress are apparent in people living in the affected areas. Large areas of agricultural land are still excluded from use due to contamination. Despite its risks, atomic power is very efficient and continues to be used in many places throughout the world.

## Applying Critical Thinking Skills

1. Why is the use of nuclear energy controversial?
2. Do you think the benefits of nuclear power outweigh the potential dangers?
3. During the Cold War in the 1900s, the United States and the Soviet Union built up stores of atomic weapons. At the end of the Cold War, they reached agreements to limit the number of atomic weapons. Do you think all countries should agree to limit atomic weapons? Explain.

# Phosphates—Help or Hazard?

Phosphorus is part of who you are—from your cells to your teeth and bones to your genetic blueprint material, DNA. Phosphorus, in the form of phosphates, is used by every living organism's cells in the transfer of energy.

## Phosphates in Detergents

Phosphates were used in the mid- to late-twentieth century, as laundry detergent additives to boost the dirt-removing agents in the soap and to soften hard water. But phosphates soon made their way into lakes and streams, causing algae to feed on the phosphate compounds and grow out of control. This growth, known as an algal bloom, kills fish and other aquatic life by using up all the available oxygen.

Phosphate detergents accounted for 30 to 70 percent of Canada's phosphate pollution in the years before 1970. By the mid-1980s, many local governments in the United States had banned the use of phosphates in detergents.

## The Mining Process

The United States, however, still faces phosphate pollution problems—this time from the mining and manufacturing of phosphate fertilizers. China, Morocco, Russia, and the United States are world suppliers of phosphates used for fertilizers and other commercial needs. Florida produces 30 percent of the world's supply of phosphate fertilizers and 75 percent of this nation's supply.

Phosphates are found naturally in phosphate rock. Manufacturers mine phosphate and prepare it for refining. The rock is crushed to make dry fertilizers or treated with sulfuric acid, a chemical agent. Nearly 90 percent of phosphate is mined for fertilizer and to make supplements for animal feed. The remaining 10 percent is used in making industrial chemicals.

## Good News and Bad News

Phosophate mining and fertilizer production are not friendly to the environment. When phosphates are treated at fertilizer manufacturing plants, fluorine gas is released. During the late 1960s, fluorine emissions killed fish and caused crippling diseases in livestock. Crops were damaged and, in some areas of Florida, citrus trees up to 80 km away from the processing plants were destroyed.

Pollution regulations at state and federal levels helped Florida turn its toxic wastes into revenue, however. By capturing fluorine gases and concentrating them into a solution called fluorosilicic acid, fertilizer manufacturers created what they call "fresh pollution concentrate." The fresh pollution concentrate is sold to cities across the country that use it to fluoridate water supplies.

Fluoridated water helps prevent cavities. It is the most inexpensive way to deliver the benefits of fluoride. The only other way is with direct contact to your teeth either in a dentist's office or by using one of the many toothpastes or fluoride rinses available.

The fresh pollution concentrate was first sold more than three decades ago. Since that time, however, no clinical studies have been conducted on its use, and no federal safety standards are in place. Only now are health officials being pressured by public interest groups to investigate the safety of fluoridated drinking water.

## Applying Problem Solving Skills

1. What do you expect will happen to Florida's supply of phosphate rock over the next several decades? What impact will that have on the United States?

2. Do you think a federal ban on phosphates in detergents should have been enacted? Why or why not?

## Critical Thinking

# Rock Solid

Just as your ancestors used sticks, mud, and rocks to build their homes, people use stone to build structures today. Many buildings, streets, bridges, piers, and highways are made of stone.

Ninety-nine percent of all building stone is used in crushed form. Only one percent is cut into slabs or blocks, called dimension stone. The best dimension stones have few pores or openings in their surfaces. This helps them resist weathering because water can't collect, freeze, and damage the stones easily. Some of the best dimension stones are made of limestone, marble, granite, sandstone, and slate. Structures built with these stones often last hundreds of years.

Constitution Hall in Washington, D.C., was built of limestone in 1929.

### Limestone

Limestone is an excellent building stone. Even though it is hard, it can be cut in any direction without splitting. It is used in the foundations, walls, sills, steps, and floors of buildings. Limestone in its crushed form is used for building roads, making cement and plaster, smelting iron ore, making paper and glass, purifying water, and treating soil.

### Marble and Granite

Marble is an elegant building stone. It is strong as well as fire-resistant and weather-resistant. Marble is usually white, but depending on the impurities mixed with its calcite, it can be red, yellow, or green. Pure calcite marble is translucent; that is, light partially penetrates the stone and is reflected back by inside surfaces. Marble is used in buildings, monuments, and decorations. Crushed marble is used in road paving, roofing, stucco, and soaps.

Granite also has been used for building since ancient times. It is strong and highly resistant to

weathering, but it is hard to cut. It often is used in public buildings and monuments because its surface can be polished to a shine. Crushed granite is used in making concrete and rock-filled dams.

### Sandstone and Slate

Sandstone comes in many colors, from cream to red, brown, and green. A reddish-brown sandstone used for constructing houses in the eastern United States is called brownstone. Well-cemented with silica, sandstone is resistant to weathering. Because early builders found that sandstone was easy to cut with hand tools, it was a common building stone. Crushed sandstone is used in concrete. It's also used in making pottery, porcelain, glass, and abrasives.

Slate is a fine-grained rock that can be split into smooth, thin sheets. This makes it ideal for flooring and roofing. It's both long-lasting and weatherproof. Chalkboards once were made of slate. Today, crushed slate is used in road surfacing and linoleum.

## Applying Critical Thinking Skills

1. What kind of rock—igneous, metamorphic, or sedimentary—is each of the five stones described above? Classify each and explain how its ability to be cut is related to its classification.

2. If you were carving a statue and you wanted it to be white, which stone would you use? Why? If you were building a monument and you wanted to polish it, which stone would you use? Why?

## Problem Solving

# Sky-High Views

For many years, when botanists went into the field to study plant distribution, they would consult a topographic map. With the integration of computers into the everyday work of scientists, fieldwork no longer requires paper maps. Instead, researchers are using the global positioning system (GPS) in conjunction with the geographic information system (GIS). The GIS lets scientists convert data into maps.

To use GPS, scientists need a receiver about the size of a cell phone that picks up a signal sent by a system of 24 satellites. This allows scientists to determine their location to within 10 m. The location is displayed on a screen for immediate viewing and can be downloaded later to computers equipped with GIS maps. Recently, the GPS/GIS system has been modified to include video taken on the ground or from the air. This allows scientists to record videotaped data along with the exact location in which the video was shot.

### A Variety of Uses

Positioning technology is having a great impact on research methods. In Colorado, botanists are using GPS and video cameras attached to airplanes to survey aspen groves and record the exact location of each grove.

Farmers can attach portable GPS receivers to their tractors. The GPS unit can determine the tractor's exact location. Other sensors can record important factors, such as soil nutrient level or water content. This information can be relayed to an on-site personal computer. Farmers can use these data to make decisions about using fertilizer or irrigation. This new technology is called precision agriculture.

Some environmental health departments are using the system to create maps of potential sources of pollution. When there is a report of contamination, these maps help officials quickly identify the source of the pollution and prevent further contamination.

### Advantages over Traditional Maps

While it does not replace traditional maps, the GPS/GIS system has several advantages. First, satellites can pinpoint locations with more accuracy. Second, with airplane-recorded video, a much larger area can be observed in a short period of time. GPS receivers record data in great detail, allowing scientists to zoom in on a small area without distorting details. Finally, video recording allows scientists to provide much more detailed data than simple field notes do. As more scientists become familiar with the technology, these methods of fieldwork will have even more applications.

## Applying Problem Solving Skills

1.  When using traditional maps, the mapped area decreases as the detail increases. This might force a scientist in the field to carry numerous maps. How can a GPS receiver help a field scientist overcome this problem?

2.  When fighting wildfires, often the commander directs many different groups of firefighters at different remote locations. How might GPS/GIS aid the commander?

3.  What might be some disadvantages of using aerial photography with GPS rather than on-the-ground observation when monitoring fern growth in a forest ecosystem?

4.  Propose another application of GPS/GIS technology.

# Saving the Soil

Soil is a vibrant, changeable substance made up of many important nutrients. These nutrients, such as phosphorus, carbon, and nitrogen, make it possible for crops and other plants to grow and thrive. Many factors, including the types of plants grown and the way farmers grow them, can change the composition of soil—for better or worse.

## Problem Practices

Some popular methods of farming can rob soil of valuable nutrients or deposit harmful elements. For example, irrigation of crops in many places can cause excess salt deposits and pesticide residues to accumulate in soil, making it unsuitable for farming. Poorly managed irrigation also can lead to soil erosion. Experts today believe that often it is better to work with a soil's natural dry state, rather than to try to change it through irrigation.

## Dryland Farming

Dryland farming is a traditional agricultural technique used in semiarid areas that don't need irrigation. Irrigation can use up sources of groundwater in as few as 35 years. Dryland farming uses only small amounts of fertilizer compared with irrigation farming.

In dryland farming, a crop-fallow rotation is used to conserve nutrients and water. This means that a farmer will leave part, usually half, of the farmland unplanted for one growing season. The unplanted ground is called fallow. The farmer then tills the stubble left by the previous crop into the ground. As the nitrogen in the crop stubble breaks down into nitrate, the fallow ground gains nutrients. Adding small amounts of fertilizer can further increase the amount of nitrate available in the soil.

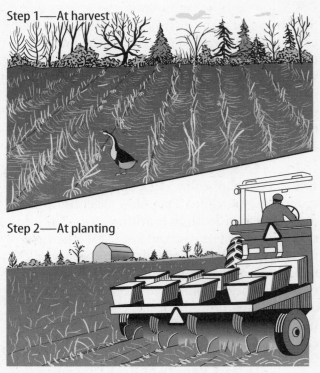

Step 1—At harvest

Step 2—At planting

**Dryland farming**

### Drawbacks and Solutions

Dryland farming potentially raises nitrate levels in groundwater. While land lies fallow, nitrate from the crop stubble can be carried to groundwater by rain or melting snow. High levels of nitrate in drinking water can cause serious health problems in humans.

Dryland farming can be improved through conservation tillage. With this method, a farmer does not remove crop stubble from fallow land. Instead, the farmer leaves the crop stubble alone and seeds the next crop on top of the stubble. Conservation tillage can increase crop yields, extend the growing season, and reduce runoff of nitrates by rainfall by up to 60 percent.

## Applying Critical Thinking Skills

1. Dryland farming can be an environmental problem when nitrates are released into groundwater. How can dryland farming be an environmental advantage? Explain.

2. In what areas of the United States might experts recommend dryland farming?

# Buffering Against Erosion

In the 1930s, huge dust storms swept through the Great Plains in the southwestern United States. The thick clouds of dust were a result of the erosion of once-fertile farmland. The erosion was caused by poor farming techniques and an eight-year drought in the area. Farmers who had settled in the region used techniques that were not suited to this dry, treeless area. Overtilling and overgrazing, combined with the drought, eroded the fertile topsoil.

In response, in 1935, Congress declared soil erosion to be a national problem and created the Soil Conservation Service. The U.S. government paid farmers to practice soil-conserving farming techniques. Today, around the world, erosion remains a key cause of desertification. Desertification is the process by which fertile land becomes arid or desert land. It is brought about by a climate change or mismanagement of the land.

### Erosion and Pollution

Erosion also can contribute to pollution. Erosion caused by storm runoff can carry chemicals such as fertilizers, pesticides, and herbicides into surface water. Scientists have found that natural wetlands filter much of the possible contamination resulting from agricultural runoff. They have applied this knowledge to farming. Farmers plant areas next to waterways in their fields with native plants rather than crops. The two main types, forest buffers and grass buffers, capture much of the sediment and chemicals that normally drain off of farmland in rainwater.

Grass and forest buffers also help control nitrate levels in the soil and groundwater. The buffers' roots encourage the growth of bacteria in the soil. These bacteria eat nitrates and other chemicals deposited by fertilizers into the groundwater. They convert the nitrates into atmospheric nitrogen, reducing nitrate levels by up to 50 percent.

### Reducing Runoff

Grass waterways and grass hedges can be used to prevent erosion in areas with heavy rainfall. By building grass-covered pathways at the lowest level of a patch of farmland, farmers can divert rainfall to these pathways, away from their crops. Because the waterways are covered by grass, topsoil from them does not easily wash away. Grass hedges go further, trapping sediment from runoff as water flows through them. In addition, the hedges slow the pace of runoff, reducing its physical effects on the land.

Forest buffers can be natural or managed. A managed forest buffer has three zones. The first zone, extending at least 4.5 m from a stream, consists of native hardwood trees. The second zone measures at least 6 m wide and contains conifers, hardwood trees, or shrubs. The third zone, a grass pathway, lies between the second zone and the crop field. All three zones filter sediments and chemicals from runoff.

Buffers provide more benefits than just controlling farm runoff. Grass buffers also can be harvested as feed for livestock. They can be used to control erosion on construction sites and in urban recreation areas. Zone two of forest buffers can be harvested for timber or other forest products.

## Applying Problem Solving Skills

1. How are wetlands, grass buffers, and forest buffers alike? How do they differ?
2. Buffers alone cannot replace wise farming methods. Explain why.
3. Without any buffers in place, where do you think farm runoff would end up? What do you think the effects of this runoff would be?

# Life on Mars?

With enough data, one day scientists might be able to finally answer the age-old question: Is there really life on Mars? In hopes of learning more about the possibility of life on Mars, scientists have been studying the geology of the red planet and have found some striking similarities to Earth.

### Evidence of an Ancient Ocean

Data about Mars have been collected since 1997 by a spacecraft known as the *Mars Global Surveyor*. Using a laser, scientists collected altimetry data, or measurements of the altitude of Mars' shorelines. Scientists now theorize that ancient Mars was, indeed, home to an ocean that covered one-quarter of its surface.

Three important pieces of information confirm this belief: (1) the shoreline is level as it would be if an ocean were present; (2) the area that would have been the ocean floor is smoother than other parts of the planet; and (3) the volume of water needed to fill the space thought to be the ocean is equal to the amount of water estimated to have existed on Mars. Scientists will continue to analyze new data sent by *Surveyor* to support or disprove the ocean hypothesis.

### A Cosmic Bar Code

In addition, geologists have found evidence to suggest that Mars has something else in common with Earth—plate tectonics. Using a magnetometer, *Surveyor* collected thousands of magnetic readings that formed a pattern some have called a "cosmic bar code." The bar code is a series of magnetic stripes that run parallel to each other. These stripes are remarkably similar to the magnetic stripes found on Earth. Furthermore, the magnetic poles on the stripes alternate from north to south, just like Earth's do. In fact, Earth's magnetic stripes are a key indicator of plate tectonics or geological shifts in the ocean floor.

Tectonic forces cause something called seafloor spreading. Seafloor spreading is created when an ocean floor moves apart to make room for hot magma that bubbles up from below. Some scientists believe that the magnetic striping found on Mars, along with the evidence showing that Mars possibly had its own ocean, proves that seafloor spreading also occurred on Mars.

### Scientists Disagree

Enough differences exist between Earth and Mars that not all scientists agree about plate tectonics on Mars. For one thing, the magnetic stripes on Mars are much wider than the stripes on Earth. And, while magnetic patterns lie along all of Earth's ocean floors, on Mars, scientists found magnetic striping only on the southern hemisphere. Also, the core of Mars, unlike Earth's core, has cooled. That means tectonic forces no longer take place on Mars.

## Applying Problem Solving Skills

1. Why is a smooth surface associated with the bottom of the ocean?

2. How does the presence of an ocean help answer the question about the possibility of life on Mars?

3. If plate tectonics is, or was, present on Mars, what other types of geological formations or occurrences might you expect to find?

4. What other types of evidence, besides magnetic patterns, might you expect from a planet with plate tectonics?

5. As head of a research project, what would you do next to try to confirm the existence of life on Mars?

 **Critical Thinking**

# Detecting Earthquake Patterns

People have tried to predict earthquakes since the earliest times. The Roman general Pliny the Elder theorized that earthquakes could be predicted using these four warnings signs: (1) buildings that tremble slightly, (2) a low cloud spread over a wide area, (3) well water that becomes cloudy and stinks, and (4) animals that behave strangely.

### Animal Sense

Although Pliny's theory was never proven, people have observed the strange behavior of animals before many earthquakes. In early Greece, one historian noted the mass exit of many animals from the city of Helice. Five days after the animals began leaving, the city was destroyed by an earthquake.

Animals might detect the tremors that precede an earthquake, or they might behave strangely because of escaping gases caused by tectonic activity. Perhaps animals behave differently because they sense a change in the weather.

### Seismic Signs

Of course, scientists don't rely solely on animal behavior to predict earthquakes. They study the history of areas to determine whether a cycle of earthquakes exists. They measure the speed of seismic waves and changes in the electrical resistance of rocks in major fault areas. They examine the levels of radon and carbon dioxide in water. They identify areas in earthquake-prone regions that have not recently released seismic strain.

In 1975, seismologists successfully predicted that an earthquake would strike Haicheng,

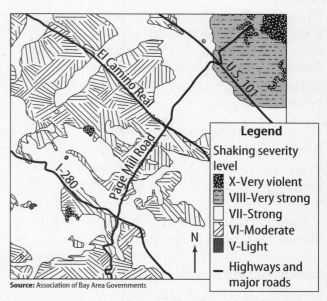

**Legend**
Shaking severity level
X-Very violent
VIII-Very strong
VII-Strong
VI-Moderate
V-Light
Highways and major roads

**Source:** Association of Bay Area Governments

**This map shows the expected shaking intensity for Palo Alto, California, if an earthquake of 6.9 on the Richter Scale were to hit.**

China. They did it by using scientific instruments and the observations of people who lived there. People reported frequent tremors and tilting of the ground. Furthermore, they reported that hibernating snakes awoke and fled their holes. Finally, about 12 h before the earthquake hit, the signs occurred so frequently that it seemed clear that an earthquake was likely. Thousands of people were evacuated from the area, and only a few people were killed when the earthquake struck.

Not all earthquakes, however, are preceded by such clear signs. An earthquake struck the city of Kobe, Japan, in 1995 without warning. In a quake that lasted only 20 s, nearly 6,400 people lost their lives, 35,000 were injured, and 400,000 were left homeless.

## Applying Critical Thinking Skills

1. Is it wise to rely on strange animal behavior as a sign for an upcoming earthquake? Explain.

2. At present, scientists can make fairly accurate, long-term predictions of earthquakes. Do you think it's possible for them to develop accurate, short-term predictions? Explain.

3. Millions of dollars are spent on prediction research. Should this money be used for other purposes? Why or why not?

## Critical Thinking

# Energy from Earth

Hydrothermal energy, a type of geothermal energy, originates deep in the earth. It heats water, which rises to Earth's surface and escapes through gaps. These outlets are found in the ground around volcanoes that are dormant or nearing extinction.

### Hydrothermal Formations

A hot spring forms where there is a lot of high-temperature water and a wide opening to the surface. It bubbles continuously with hot water and dissolved minerals.

In places where there is little hot water and a narrow opening to the surface, a fumarole (FYEW muh rohl) forms. When water changes from a liquid to a vapor in an instant, it flashes into steam and expands, taking up 1,600 times more space than the water. The steam moves up and drives the gases through the narrow opening.

A solfatara (sohl fuh TAHR uh) is a type of fumarole that emits steam and sulfurous gases. The areas around solfataras are rich with sulfur deposits.

Mud pots are bubbling pools of extremely hot mud. They form in spots where hot water combines with dissolved rock. They can form low cones, called mud volcanoes.

Another kind of hydrothermal formation is a geyser. Scientists theorize that a geyser's underground channels are different from those of hot springs, fumaroles, and mud pots. Trapped in a complex system of tubes and pockets, water heats far beyond its normal boiling point. The superheated water expands, forcing some of the water toward the surface. This reduces the pressure on the superheated water below. The water then flashes to steam,

which shoots to the surface, carrying water with it. Geysers are rare. They occur in groups only in Iceland, New Zealand, Indonesia, and Yellowstone National Park in Wyoming and Idaho.

### Tapping Earth's Power

The world's largest energy resource, geothermal energy, can generate electricity, warm greenhouses, and heat and cool homes. Geothermal energy is clean energy because its power plants do not emit nitrogen oxides and release only low levels of sulfur dioxide and carbon dioxide. If the energy can be captured, geothermal resources have the potential to provide nearly limitless, pollution-free energy.

**A fumarole ejects water vapor and other gases, such as carbon dioxide and hydrogen sulfide.**

## Applying Critical Thinking Skills

1. How does the amount of groundwater affect the formation of a hot spring, a fumarole, and a mud pot?

2. What would be some advantages of a geothermal power plant compared with burning coal or using nuclear power?

# Xenotime Dating

In an attempt to predict Earth's future accurately, geologists need to understand the past. By looking at various rocks and determining when and where they formed, scientists can learn about Earth's formation and its changing structure.

## Limited Accuracy

The most common method of dating rocks is by measuring the rate of radioactive decay of carbon in the rocks. Unfortunately, this method has not proven successful in dating rocks formed during Earth's first 4 billion years, the Precambrian time. Since Earth is only 4.6 billion years old, scientists are left guessing about what happened during most of Earth's existence.

Scientists have a relatively good understanding of the most recent 600 million years on Earth. This is due primarily to the rapid increase in the number of living organisms during that time and the fossils that they left. During the first 4 billion years on Earth, however, what little life existed was small and left few fossils.

The fact that many Precambrian rocks are sedimentary, formed largely from debris left by other rocks, adds to this problem. In the past, scientists could date such rocks only by measuring the age of volcanic rocks around the sedimentary

rocks if, in fact, any existed. Using this method, scientists could say that the sedimentary rock formed between the dates when the volcanic rocks formed.

## New Dating Method

A new technique, called xenotime dating, is helping scientists more accurately date rocks of the Precambrian time. Xenotime dating gives scientists a more precise method for dating sedimentary rocks by determining when sediments in the rocks were deposited.

Xenotime, a phosphate mineral found in most sedimentary rocks, forms relatively shortly after sediments are deposited. Initially, xenotime contains little lead but large amounts of uranium. As time passes, the uranium decays, forming more lead. By measuring the amount of lead existing in a sample of xenotime, scientists can determine the age of the rock containing the sample.

This new process of radioactive dating will help scientists date sedimentary rock and give them a better understanding of tectonic processes and plate positions. A better understanding of how Earth's crust has moved in the past could prove valuable in predicting how it might move in the future.

## Applying Problem Solving Skills

1. Scientists have shown that lead does not move from one crystal of xenotime into another. If it did, how would that affect xenotime dating?

2. A geologist discovers a formation with two layers of sediment. The top layer shows a lead measurement of 27, and the bottom layer shows a measurement of 14. Analyze these data to determine the relative ages of the layers, and propose an explanation for the position of the sediments.

3. Earth's existence can be separated into four time periods. From youngest to oldest, they are the Cenozoic era, the Mesozoic era, the Paleozoic era, and the Precambrian time. Sequence the time periods by the amount of lead in the xenotime you would expect to find in sedimentary rocks from each time period. Explain your sequence.

## Problem Solving

# Birds and Dinosaurs— Related or Not?

Can you learn about dinosaurs by watching birds at a feeder? Scientists generally agree that dinosaurs were a type of reptile and that birds descended from reptiles. Scientists don't agree, however, on how closely birds are related to dinosaurs.

### Comparing Traits

To see how closely related birds might be to dinosaurs, scientists compare and contrast living birds with fossils of primitive species that might be related to birds. Using complex computer programs, they look for matches in at least 80 physical traits of modern birds. These traits include the skull, teeth, neck, pelvis, tail, shoulder, bones, hands, feet, ankles, and stance.

Scientists have found several species of dinosaurs that had feathers. Several other dinosaur species have bones similar to modern birds—and unlike any other living animal. Some dinosaurs also had wrists that could bend in a flapping motion, like a wing, and toes that were arranged so they could grasp branches.

### Mismatched Traits

Other traits make some scientists question the relationship between birds and dinosaurs. After studying photographs of dinosaur fossils, some scientists believe the abdominal cavity of several birdlike dinosaurs was more like those of modern-day crocodiles than birds. Crocodiles have a division in the chest cavity that allows the lungs to fill with air. When muscles attached to the liver and diaphragm contract, air is pulled into the lungs. Birds, in contrast, do not have this system. They have lungs that allow air to flow through them without the help of a diaphragm.

### Not a Simple Question

Before deciding if there's a link between birds and dinosaurs, scientists still must answer several questions. Were dinosaurs cold-blooded (like reptiles) or warm-blooded (like birds)? Some dinosaurs with feathers probably could not fly. If so, did the feathers develop to attract mates, or did they develop to insulate the dinosaurs? If the feathers could keep the dinosaurs warm, the dinosaurs must have been warm-blooded.

It's likely that only one-fourth of all dinosaurs have been found in the fossil record so far. That means that many links between birds and dinosaurs or between birds and another ancestor have yet to be found.

## Applying Problem Solving Skills

1. How would you define *bird*, if a dinosaur with feathers is not a bird?

2. A species called *Microraptor zhaoianus* had feathers and toes that could have grasped tree branches, yet it probably could not fly. It had lightweight bones similar in structure to modern-day birds' bones. It had a long tail like a dinosaur's, and its teeth were arranged like those of a dinosaur. Other dinosaur "birds" were much larger, however. *Microraptor* was about as big as a crow. Does any of this information help you answer the following questions: Are birds modern-day dinosaurs? Were dinosaurs cold- or warm-blooded? Did birds learn to fly from the ground up or from the trees down? Explain.

# Keeping the Atmosphere Healthy

In the late 1800s and early 1900s, the first refrigerators used toxic gases as coolants. These gases caused fatal accidents when leaks occurred. In 1928, chlorofluorocarbons (CFCs) were first synthesized as safer chemicals for refrigerators. CFCs are nontoxic, nonflammable, and stable gases. The stability of CFCs, however, poses a threat to the ozone layer.

### CFCs' Negative Side

CFCs were formerly used in aerosol sprays, blowing agents for foams, cleaning solvents, and as refrigerants in air conditioners. But in the 1980s, a hole was discovered in the ozone layer over Antarctica, and CFCs were determined to be the culprit. The ozone layer lies in the stratosphere, which is about 15 km to 40 km above Earth. Ozone absorbs a type of ultraviolet light, UVB, which is harmful to living organisms. UVB causes skin cancers and cataracts, as well as damage to some marine organisms and plants.

In 1987, an international agreement was signed by 27 nations requiring industrialized countries to cut their production of CFCs in half before the year 2000. Exemptions were approved for production of CFCs in developing countries.

### Scientific Solutions

Many substitutes for CFCs already exist. Efforts are being made to find more substitutes and to construct equipment that doesn't rely on CFCs. In Arizona, for example, scientists are working on an air conditioner that uses freshwater and salt water as its working fluids.

In refrigerators, CFCs circulate in pipes inside the refrigerator and also are part of the foam insulation used in the outside shell. Manufacturers are interested in tetrafluoroethane and other substitutes for CFCs, but they need more than CFC replacements to meet efficiency requirements. New insulation ideas include using silica gels, silica powders, stainless-steel sheets with glass beads between them welded together by a laser, and microfiberglass.

Substitutes for CFCs need to be reviewed by the Environmental Protection Agency, and inventions will have to be tested. Scientists hope that new methods will be developed to protect the ozone layer.

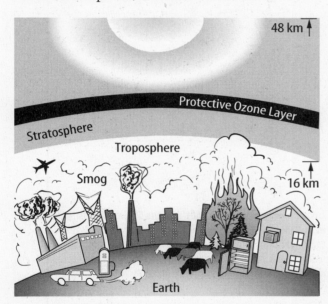

While ozone close to Earth's surface is a pollutant, the ozone layer protects life on Earth.

## Applying Critical Thinking Skills

1. The 1987 international agreement was based partly on the assumption that industrialized nations produced a much greater amount of CFCs than less-industrialized nations. That was one of the reasons the agreement required industrialized nations to cut their production of hydrocarbons, but didn't require less-industrialized nations to limit their production. Do you think that was a good agreement? Explain.

2. Suppose you're an engineer with an idea for a new air conditioner. What kind of factors should you consider when developing and testing your idea?

**Problem Solving**

# Snowball Earth

Rocks deposited by glaciers can be found all over the world, even in tropical areas. This fact has led some scientists to hypothesize that Earth, at some time, might have been completely frozen. Evidence shows that a total global freeze might have happened as many as four or even five times. Scientists call these global freezes "Snowball Earth" and believe that they most likely occurred between 580 million and 750 million years ago.

### Why did Earth freeze?

One possible explanation for why this happened lies with the plate tectonics theory. According to this theory, the same forces under Earth's surface that cause earthquakes and volcanoes cause the continental plates to move around. The continents have moved together and moved apart and are, in fact, still moving.

Before Snowball Earth, the continents were one giant continent, located near the equator. The continent's interior, far away from the oceans, was dry. Then, this large continent broke into three pieces, still near the equator. Now, however, the interiors of the continents were much closer to the oceans, causing rain to fall. The increased rainfall caused more carbon dioxide to wash out of the air, causing Earth's temperatures to drop, and ice sheets to form in the polar regions.

As huge polar ice sheets grew larger, their glaring white surfaces reflected the Sun's heat away from Earth, making temperatures fall even more. Once ice had covered half of Earth's surface, so

much of the Sun's radiation was deflected, that temperatures on Earth plunged. This caused the ice sheets to grow even larger, until they covered Earth and its oceans completely.

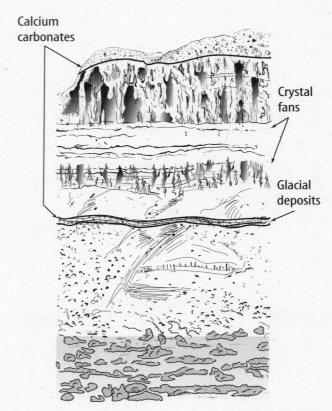

Calcium carbonates

Crystal fans

Glacial deposits

**Layers of rock in the Rocky Cliffs on the Skeleton Coast in Namibia, in southwestern Africa, provide evidence of a global freeze and rapid warming afterward. Calcium carbonates usually form in warm seas but not in glaciers. They indicate Earth did freeze, even near the equator, and then warmed up rapidly.**

## Applying Problem Solving Skills

1. During a global freeze, volcanoes would have continued to erupt. Volcanoes emit carbon dioxide, a greenhouse gas. Usually, evaporating moisture absorbs some carbon dioxide in the air. Water vapor also raises temperatures. How do you think this process would have changed with ice sheets covering all of the oceans?

2. *Albedo* is a measurement of the amount of radiation from the Sun that reflects off a surface. A higher albedo indicates that more radiation is reflected, meaning surface temperatures are lower. Note the albedos for the following surfaces: new pavement, 0.04; seawater, 0.10; forest, 0.14; dry desert, 0.37; sea ice, 0.60; and snow on ice, 0.80. Considering the effect that large ice sheets have on Earth's climate, what do you think the effect would be if dry deserts were paved over? Explain.

## Critical Thinking

# The Ocean—An Abundant Source of Salt

Much of Earth's surface is covered by water, but 94 percent of it is salt water. Because there is a lack of freshwater in parts of the world, such as the Middle East and the Caribbean, scientists have developed methods for using salt water from the ocean for drinking water. This process, called desalination, removes salt from water.

### Desalination Processes

Distillation is one of the oldest methods of desalination. Seawater is boiled to produce pure steam. The steam is cooled until it condenses and runs as pure water. Distillation has been useful at sea. U.S. Navy cruisers had distillation plants on board in World War II. A more modern version of distillation is freeze distillation. Freeze distillation removes salt and impurities from water by freezing it.

Electrodialysis is a process that uses an electric current to move salt ions through a membrane, leaving freshwater behind. It works well with brackish groundwater, because brackish water has a lower salt concentration than seawater.

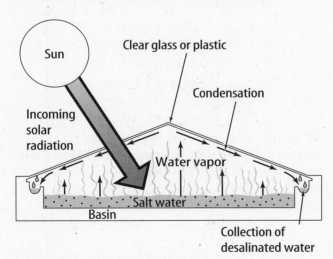

**Solar energy can be used to desalinate water.**

Reverse osmosis is a pressure-driven process. Pressure is used to separate the freshwater, which passes through a membrane, from the salts, which do not. Reverse osmosis also works better with brackish water.

The most recent development in desalination techniques is ocean thermal energy conversion or OTEC. Keahole Point on the island of Hawaii has become one of the world's foremost laboratories and test facilities for OTEC technologies. Because the layers of ocean water have different temperatures, OTEC uses the ocean's temperature differences to produce energy. This method could provide areas, such as tropical island communities, with power as well as with desalinated water.

### Environmental and Economic Concerns

Desalinating water has negative effects on the environment. The leftover salt solution might kill marine life when it is returned to the ocean. Incoming salt water might be treated with a biocide, such as chlorine, to remove algae and bacteria. These chemicals need to be treated prior to being released into the ocean.

Another disadvantage to desalination is that most of the processes are expensive to perform. Distillation costs are high due to the energy that is needed to heat the water. Reverse osmosis and electrodialysis are cheaper processes because they require less energy, but the membranes have short lives and are expensive to replace.

Although there are currently many processes for desalinating water, scientists continue to work on improving these methods. The need for low-cost desalination methods will always be in great demand for arid areas of the world.

## Applying Critical Thinking Skills

1. Why are there so many different processes for desalination? What are scientists looking for?

2. Do you think that the need for desalination will increase or decrease in the next century? Give reasons for your answer.

## Critical Thinking

# The Mysterious Eel

Eels are a snakelike fish that breed in the ocean but feed and grow in freshwater. To do this, they must migrate. Early scientists were puzzled by the eels' migration patterns. Europeans, for instance, found large numbers of adult eels in lakes, streams, and rivers. But no one ever saw a young eel or an eel egg.

The Greek philosopher Aristotle suggested that eels developed from the mud at the bottom of the lakes. It wasn't until 1922 that the mystery was solved by Danish oceanographer Johannes Schmidt. He found that a particular small, flat fish found in the Sargasso Sea was actually a young eel.

### A Moving Sea

The Sargasso Sea is an area of warm and exceptionally clear water a few hundred kilometers east of Florida. The Sargasso Sea drifts, and its location is determined by the changing,

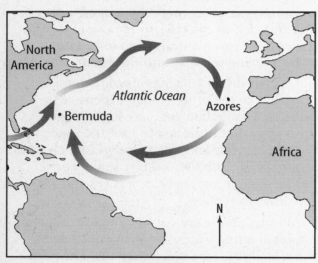

**Sargasso Sea**

clockwise-flowing ocean currents that form its perimeter. Here, about 600 m beneath the surface of the ocean, American and European eels produce and fertilize eggs. Tiny, transparent larvae hatch from these eggs. These tiny life-forms are then carried northward by ocean currents. Some are caught by currents that move up the east coast of the United States and enter freshwater rivers where they live and feed. Others are carried by the Gulf Stream across the Atlantic Ocean to Europe.

### The Eels' Life Cycle

During their drifting migration, which can take three or four years, the larvae of the European eels develop into larger, leaf-shaped larvae that feed on plankton. When they finally reach the shallow ocean waters near land, they become young eels and move into the freshwater rivers along the coastline. In freshwater, they feed and grow.

Eels can remain in freshwater from five to ten years, although eels 20 years old have been reported. An eel takes about ten years to reach maturity. At this time, it changes to a silvery color and its eyes grow larger. The mature eel moves downriver and back to the sea.

The mystery of eels is not solved, though. Adult eels have never been caught in the Sargasso Sea. Their breeding, or spawning, behavior is still unknown, although it is presumed that the adult eels die after spawning. Do they return from Europe to the Sargasso Sea? If so, why have none been seen? If not, where do the larvae in the Sargasso come from?

## Applying Critical Thinking Skills

1. Aristotle suggested that eels developed from mud at the bottom of lakes. What type of scientific evidence could you present to him to prove otherwise?

2. Parts of the life cycle of eels (and other marine animals) are still a mystery. Why does this make it important to preserve all marine habitats?

# Critical Thinking

# Plant-Based Fuels

Surplus corn and other grains, such as wheat and barley, can be processed into ethanol. A clear, colorless liquid, ethanol is used as fuel in internal-combustion engines, such as those found in automobiles. Ethanol already is blended into most gasoline sold in the United States. This use of ethanol saves nearly a billion gallons of oil a year.

## Biomass Ethanol

Scientists are investigating advanced ways, such as biomass feedstocks, to produce ethanol. The term *biomass* refers to any organic matter that is renewable, including wood, crops, plants, and animal wastes. Biomass feedstocks include corn fiber, plant residue, and rice straw. The feedstocks contain cellulose, which can be converted into sugars that are fermented into ethanol. These biomass feedstocks are considered low- or no-cost waste material.

Using inexpensive resources reduces the cost of producing ethanol. Also, using these waste materials has environmental benefits; they otherwise would be burned or put into a landfill. As an added bonus, waste materials of the ethanol conversion process are high in protein and other nutrients, making them an excellent feed ingredient for livestock.

## SoyDiesel

Biodiesel fuel is being developed as an alternative to petroleum for heavy vehicles. This fuel is made from natural, renewable sources, such as new or used vegetable oils. It is a cleaner-burning fuel and can operate in existing combustion-ignition engines. Soybean oil and methanol produce a product called methyl soyate, or SoyDiesel. SoyDiesel is the main type of biodiesel fuel used in the United States. Alternative oils that are being considered are animal fat wastes and used frying oil, which are cheaper than soybean oil.

## Methanol

Methanol is another plant-based fuel. It is made from wood. Like ethanol, methanol can be mixed with gasoline. Pure methanol, or neat methanol, is used as a racing fuel. Methanol is a promising hydrogen source for fuel-cell vehicles. Hydrogen gas also is being tested for use in combustion engines. Because it is a gas instead of liquid, it is easier to store and transport.

Both ethanol and methanol are renewable resources, which means that they can be replaced by natural processes in less than 100 years. These clean-burning fuels are promising fuel alternatives for the future.

### Ethanol Production

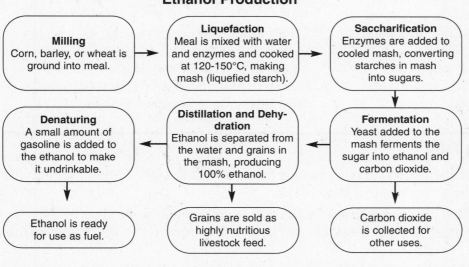

**Milling**
Corn, barley, or wheat is ground into meal.

**Liquefaction**
Meal is mixed with water and enzymes and cooked at 120-150°C, making mash (liquefied starch).

**Saccharification**
Enzymes are added to cooled mash, converting starches in mash into sugars.

**Fermentation**
Yeast added to the mash ferments the sugar into ethanol and carbon dioxide.

**Distillation and Dehydration**
Ethanol is separated from the water and grains in the mash, producing 100% ethanol.

**Denaturing**
A small amount of gasoline is added to the ethanol to make it undrinkable.

Ethanol is ready for use as fuel.

Grains are sold as highly nutritious livestock feed.

Carbon dioxide is collected for other uses.

## Applying Critical Thinking Skills

1. Why do you think some people would be reluctant to change from using gasoline or diesel fuel in their automobiles to ethanol or methanol?

2. Do you think the United States should continue working toward using renewable agricultural products for fuel energy? Why or why not?

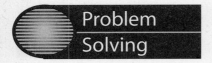

## Problem Solving

# Efforts to Neutralize Acid Precipitation

Oil- and coal-burning power plants produce pollutants. These pollutants, in particular sulfur dioxide and nitrogen oxide, contribute to haze in the air and can cause health problems. When they mix with rain, snow, or fog, they produce acid precipitation. Acid precipitation consists of sulfuric and nitric acids. It can damage forests, buildings, and monuments, and can acidify lakes and streams.

### Reducing Effects of Acid Precipitation

Woods Lake is in the Adirondack Mountains in New York. In 1989, it was discovered that no fish could live in the lake because it was too acidic. Acid rain fell on the soil and washed into streams that flowed into the lake. Scientists were determined to save the lake. First, they tried putting limestone slurry into the lake. Limestone is a basic material that, when added to acidic water, makes it neutral. After adding the limestone, the scientists stocked the lake with fish, but the fish didn't live. Rain brought more acid into the lake.

Then, scientists dropped large amounts of limestone pellets by helicopter onto the soil near Woods Lake. Rain washed the limestone into the lake. Acid levels in the lake dropped and rose only slightly after additional rains. Scientists estimated that the limestone pellets should work for about five years before additional applications were needed.

### Preventing Acid Precipitation

In a 1990 amendment to the Clean Air Act, Congress made a plan to reduce sulfur dioxide and nitrogen oxide emmissions by the year 2010. The goal was for companies to reduce their pollution levels by millions of tons. This new law offered a different approach. It recognized that companies would continue to pollute. However, companies that polluted less than their allowance could use what was left over as a reserve for later or they could trade it to other companies who went over their allowances.

Why did Congress take this approach? Members wanted to solve the pollution problem, while keeping the costs for doing so as low as possible. It is expensive for companies to reduce emissions. They might have to fix or replace equipment, or they might even have to change the way they use fuels. Under the new plan, companies that could afford to reduce their emissions could reduce pollution to even lower levels than required by their allowances. If so, they could trade their allowances to other companies that couldn't afford to meet their own goals. Overall, the pollution level would decrease while costs would be kept down.

This unique approach to reducing emissions worked. By 1995, sulfur dioxide emissions were almost 40 percent below target at 445 plants in 21 eastern and midwestern states. Nationally, emissions were 20 percent below target.

## Applying Problem Solving Skills

1.  The problem that concerned scientists studying Woods Lake was that the lake couldn't support life. What scientific hypothesis was tested at Woods Lake?

2.  One concern with the trading program is that it might reduce pollution in some areas of the country, while letting it increase in other areas. Do you think this program is an acceptable way to reduce pollution overall?

3.  Why is it difficult to judge the success of a pollution-control program?

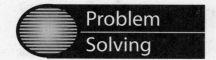

# The Pros and Cons of Gene Modification

Farmers use many different chemicals to kill insects and weeds that threaten their crops. Chemicals are a concern to many consumers because they can contaminate soil and water. Some have been found to cause cancer. Some experts claim that the disadvantages of pesticides are overemphasized. Still, scientists search for ways to avoid chemical pesticides.

## Biotechnology

One alternative to using pesticides is biotechnology. Biotechnology is a collection of scientific techniques used to create or improve plants, animals, and microorganisms.

In Colorado, the potato beetle had plagued potato crops for years. The beetles would eat an entire field of crops, leaving nothing but stems. Rather than using chemical pesticides, researchers invented a "smarter" potato. They inserted a gene that changed the DNA of the potato. It worked as an organic pesticide. Now the potato plant contains a biopesticide that is deadly to the beetle.

Altering the DNA of a plant is called genetic modification. Approximately 18 million hectares of American farmland are planted with genetically modified (GM) crops. This technology is being studied for use in areas of Asia, Latin America, and Africa where hunger and malnutrition are epidemic.

Researchers have developed a new rice that contains iron and vitamin A and a genetically altered sweet potato that resists a harvest-destroying virus. There is hope that these and other crops can be planted to help prevent malnutrition and starvation

## Untested Waters

Despite the promise of GM plants, some people fear the results. One concern is that genes of GM plants might cross-fertilize with wild plants and create "super weeds." These super weeds could become resistant to certain herbicides. Some fear that mutant bugs might result if pests become resistant to the toxic effects of GM crops.

Other concerns are for human safety. Opponents call GM crops "Frankenfood." They fear that illnesses could result from eating these plants. The greatest human health concern is allergies that might result from GM plants. Testing can be performed for known allergens, but new allergens might be created when genes in plants are altered.

**A scientific study found that pollen from one variety of GM corn might kill the caterpillar** `Danaus plexippus`**, which becomes the monarch butterfly.**

## Applying Problem Solving Skills

1. What are the major problems connected with chemical pesticides?

2. Why do some people anticipate problems with genetic modification?

3. Which type of pesticides—chemical or genetically modified—would you prefer to have used on foods you eat? Why?

4. Do you think the government should regulate genetic modification? Explain.

### Problem Solving

# Controlling the Zebra Mussel

In the mid-1980s, a mollusk new to North America, the zebra mussel, was found in Lake St. Clair in Ontario, Canada. Ordinarily, zebra mussels live in the seas of northern and western Europe. They are small, inactive creatures measuring just 2.5 to 7.5 cm long and spend their lives attached to an underwater surface. They probably came here from the Black and Caspian seas by way of ballast water, the seawater used to maintain the stability of a ship.

**Zebra mussels attach to underwater surfaces.**

### A Growing Problem

At first there were only a few small colonies, but within months the mussels expanded throughout Lake St. Clair and into surrounding lakes. They spread to Lake Erie and into the other Great Lakes. Zebra mussels have been found in portions of the Mississippi, Hudson, Ohio, Illinois, Tennessee, Susquehanna, and Arkansas rivers. They have spread to at least 19 states, including California.

Studies estimate that one female zebra mussel can release one million eggs per year. To survive, they eat large amounts of plankton. Each day, a single adult mussel can consume all of the plankton found in a liter of water.

### Other Species Suffer

When enough zebra mussels colonize one area, they leave little or no food for the native animals that also live on plankton. This produces a shortage of food for larger fish. Because zebra mussels eat most of the plankton, lake water becomes clearer so more light reaches deeper into the lake, causing increases in vegetation such as algae.

Zebra mussels tend to attach themselves to any available surface. Because they multiply so rapidly, they have been found throughout water-treatment plants on the Great Lakes, clinging to pipes and machinery. They decrease the diameter of the pipes' openings and in some cases cut off the flow of water.

### Solutions

Several methods exist for removing zebra mussels. The safest way is to remove them by hand, but that takes a great deal of time. Some water-treatment plants use jets of steam and hot water to kill them. Most treatment plants use chlorine. This works, but too much chlorine can contaminate drinking water. Scientists have been testing potassium, bromine, ozone, and ultraviolet light as possible alternatives.

In addition, scientists have suggested introducing exotic predators to help control the growth of zebra mussels. Another solution would be to regulate the spawning of zebra mussels. If they could be made to spawn at times when plankton levels are low, the larvae would die.

## Applying Problem Solving Skills

1. Consider the problem of ridding North America of zebra mussels. Give advantages and disadvantages of each of the methods mentioned. Which method described would you recommend?

2. Ridding the lakes and rivers of zebra mussels will be expensive. Where do you think the money for such a project should come from? Write a statement defending your answer.

 **Problem Solving**

# Recycling in Space

You probably have participated in water-saving projects at home or in your community. Such projects usually include taking shorter showers, turning off the tap when not necessary, and reusing dishwater or bathwater to water plants or the lawn. What if you also had to recycle the moisture in your breath, sweat, or even urine?

### Water in Space
Astronauts on the International Space Station (ISS) have to do just that. In addition, they also must reuse the humidity generated by any animals on board, such as lab rats. Although some water and food supplies will be carried to the station by shuttle missions, it's too expensive to ship all of the water needed. The Environmental Control and Life Support System (ECLSS) Water Recycling System (WRS) will recycle most of the water used on board. This will save more than 18,000 kg of water per year, which would otherwise have to be brought in by shuttle missions.

### Purer than Water on Earth
Of course, the water you drink on Earth also comes partly from recycled breath, sweat, and urine. Wastewater that flows into the ground passes through the soil, which filters it physically. Microbes in the soil act on organic substances, filtering the water chemically. Waste-water that evaporates into the atmosphere leaves impurities behind and is converted to rain—nearly pure freshwater.

On the ISS, machines do the work of all of these natural processes. Machines that break down can be fixed, unlike microbes, which can die or grow out of control. The system uses three steps. First, a filter removes particles larger than water molecules. Then the wastewater passes through layers that remove impurities. Finally, a catalytic oxidation reactor removes volatile organic compounds and kills bacteria and viruses.

The life-support system is not perfect, however. Over time, water will be lost in several ways. The water-purification system itself will produce some unusable water as brine, and the air-purification systems will remove some humidity that could have been transformed into water. When astronauts go outside the ISS, some air containing humidity will flow out through the air locks.

Engineers hope to increase the efficiency of the water-purification system to 95 percent. This way, the moisture contained in food supplies would replace the other five percent.

### Clearing the Air
The ECLSS also purifies the air astronauts breathe on the ISS. Humans and animals breathe in oxygen and breathe out carbon dioxide. Currently, the system vents $CO_2$ to the outside. Eventually, engineers hope to recycle carbon dioxide. Humans and animals also emit small amounts of other gases such as ammonia and methane. Scientific experiments also create vapors that must be removed from the air. Activated charcoal filters will remove these gases.

Where will the oxygen come from? In a process called electrolysis, solar panels on the ISS will create electricity which, in turn, splits water into hydrogen gas and oxygen gas. On Earth, this process occurs as part of photosynthesis.

## Applying Problem Solving Skills

1. How does the method of purifying water on the ISS differ from natural purification methods on Earth?
2. Eventually, engineers hope to use plants in space to create oxygen and filter the air. Why do you think they now use machines?

### Critical Thinking

# Fighting Off the Winter Blues

When winter approaches and the weather gets colder and the days get shorter, many people experience a noticeable change in their moods. They may oversleep, overeat, or experience depression, fatigue, or difficulty concentrating. Although these symptoms can have many causes, they often are the symptoms of a disease called seasonal affective disorder or SAD.

### Who Suffers?

It is estimated that 10 million to 25 million Americans experience symptoms of SAD. People of all ages, occupations, and ethnic groups can suffer from SAD. Most sufferers, however, are women between the ages of 20 and 50. Almost four times as many women as men suffer from the disease.

Some people might have only a mild form of the disease. They might feel slightly depressed. They could oversleep and overeat. They might lack energy. Some people suffer from much stronger cases of SAD. Some can't concentrate during the winter. Some are totally nonproductive, lacking enough energy to do even the simplest tasks. They might withdraw from social contact and feel depressed constantly.

As winter ends, SAD sufferers begin to recover. Once again, they participate fully in their daily routines. Yet, year after year, SAD symptoms reappear in winter.

### The Light Connection

Scientists are researching the causes of SAD. They think there is a link between SAD and the decreased amount of daylight available during

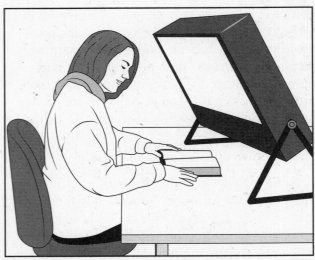
Light therapy helps people overcome the effects of SAD.

the winter. Light affects hormone levels. Some scientists think that it's this shortness of daylight hours that causes SAD.

### Light Therapy

Researchers reason that if a lack of light causes SAD, light therapy could help SAD sufferers. Initial studies had groups of SAD patients sitting in front of light boxes for several hours a day before dawn and after dusk. The light boxes used a type of fluorescent light that's similar to the color range of natural summer sunlight.

The patients began to see positive changes soon after the treatments started. Their moods began to improve. They had more energy and felt able to carry on their everyday activities. The same patients were exposed to periods of dim light as well. The dim-light therapy proved to be ineffective.

## Applying Critical Thinking Skills

1. People who live in the higher latitudes are more likely to suffer from SAD than people who live in the lower latitudes. Why do you think this is?

2. SAD patients using light therapy can suffer from side effects such as headache, eyestrain, and sleeplessness. What might be done to reduce these side effects?

 Critical Thinking

# Early Skywatchers

Many researchers study early peoples and their knowledge of the Sun, Moon, and stars. This field of study, called archaeoastronomy, focuses on peoples from prehistoric times to the Egyptians and Maya.

These scientists have learned that the early people of the Americas were excellent astronomers and builders. The Maya built the oldest known observatory in the western hemisphere around A.D. 317. They kept careful records of the movements and changes of the Sun and Moon on calendars. Astronomy was the study of their gods. To the skywatchers, the apparent movements of the Sun and Moon gave the gods their personalities. The events in the sky were reflected in the religion, festivals, art, and architecture of the people.

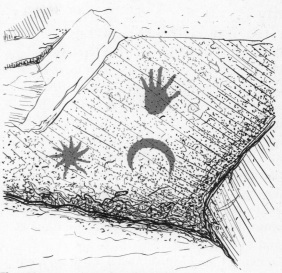

**The 1054 supernova rock at Chaco Canyon**

## Machu Picchu

At one site, Machu Picchu in Peru, archaeoastronomers study the Incan temple of Torreón. An amazing occurrence takes place there on the June solstice. Shortly after dawn, the sunlight shines through a window onto a sacred stone. The Inca believed that the Sun god was returning to its home on the June solstice. They held a Sun festival at that time to pay special honor to the Sun god.

## Teotihuacan

The Toltec city Teotihuacan lies northeast of Mexico City, Mexico. Teotihuacan was already in ruins when the Aztecs ruled central Mexico. The Toltecs arranged their city in a huge, four-part grid. Within one grid is the great Temple of the Sun, which was built over a sacred cave. Its steps align with a point on the horizon. Scientists have found that this point is the place where the Pleiades star cluster sets on the horizon.

## Chaco Canyon

Chaco Canyon in New Mexico was probably a cultural center to ancestral Puebloan residents from about A.D. 900 through A.D. 1130. Ancient drawings found in West Mesa, a part of Chaco Canyon, contain three symbols—a large star, a crescent moon, and a print of a hand. Every 18.5 years, the Moon and Earth are positioned so that they can be seen from West Mesa. The fingers of the handprint point to the Moon in the sky on that day. Archaeoastronomers believe that the large star in the drawing is Crab Nebula, which was formed during the A.D. 1054 supernova. Did the Chacoans see the supernova and record it in their drawings or is there some other explanation?

Archaeoastronomers are trying to answer this and many other questions. By studying the drawings and temples of early peoples, people today might gain a better understanding and appreciation of early skywatchers.

## Applying Critical Thinking Skills

1. How are the three monuments described in this passage alike?

2. What evidence supports the statement that the early people of the Americas were excellent astronomers and builders?

3. Why do you think scientists are interested in the astronomy of early peoples?

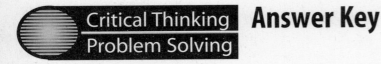

# Critical Thinking Problem Solving — Answer Key

## Activity 1 _____ page 1
### Earth's Last Frontier—Hydrothermal Vents

1. **Distinguishing Relevant from Irrelevant Facts:** Students should list at least three questions that they would have asked the first scientist to see a hydrothermal vent. Questions might be related to the vent's appearance, the life-forms surrounding it, the methods used to find it, or any other appropriate subject.

2. **Recognizing Cause and Effect:** By discovering the unique bacteria that were at the base of the food web, scientists could begin to understand how this extreme environment could support so many life-forms.

3. **Drawing Conclusions:** Answers will vary, but students should indicate that hydrothermal vents are Earth's last frontier because they have not been fully explored. It has been less than 30 years since the vents were first discovered and exploration has been slow. In comparison to space exploration, scientists know little about this phenomenon.

## Activity 2 _____ page 2
### Atomic Energy—Good and Bad

1. **Drawing Conclusions:** Nuclear energy can provide power for generating electricity, but the fear of accidents has caused many people to object to its use.

2. **Making Judgments:** Students' answers might vary. Students should illustrate an understanding of the potential benefits and dangers of atomic power.

3. **Developing a Perspective:** Students' answers might vary. Students should weigh their concerns for safety with the need for power.

## Activity 3 _____ page 3
### Phosphates—Help or Hazard?

1. **Making Predictions or Interpretations:** If Florida's phosphate rock continues to be mined in large amounts, the supply eventually will run low. The United States will need to find alternative supplies for phosphate fertilizer or an alternative form of fertilizer.

2. **Making Judgments:** Students' answers will vary. Students believing that a federal ban on phosphates in detergents should have been enacted might cite its large role in causing pollution, particularly algal blooms in lakes and streams. Students believing a federal ban should not have been enacted might state that such a ban should be based on local or state conditions and therefore should be made at the local or state level.

## Activity 4 _____ page 4
### Rock Solid

1. **Classifying:** Limestone—sedimentary; granite—igneous; slate and marble—metamorphic; sandstone—sedimentary. Limestone and sandstone split easily because as sedimentary rocks, they formed in layers. Slate is a foliated metamorphic rock; it formed in layers also. Granite, an igneous rock, and marble, a nonfoliated metamorphic rock, form not in layers but in solid masses; they would be more difficult to cut.

2. **Evaluating Information:** Marble would be a good choice for the statue because it can be found in pure white, it carves well, and its translucence has made it a valued sculpture material in the past. Granite would be a good choice for the monument because its surface can be polished to a shine.

## Activity 5 _____ page 5
### Sky-High Views

1. **Evaluating Information:** A GPS receiver has a high resolution. Thus, one computerized databank provides enough information to produce detailed local maps of a large area. The positions can then be mapped on an electronic map of choice.

2. **Observing and Inferring:** It would give the commander the locations of all the groups' positions at any one time and reduce the time needed to redistribute the groups. Aerial photography also might be useful in tracking the exact location of the fire as it spreads.

## Answer Key (continued)

3. **Comparing and Contrasting:** In monitoring fern growth in a dense forest, aerial photography would not be a good choice because ferns grow low to the ground and the trees would obscure their view.
4. **Making Predictions or Interpretations:** Students' answers might vary. Some potential applications might include surveying land for building projects, mapping problem traffic areas, or producing more accurate ocean navigation maps.

## Activity 6 _____ page 6
### Saving the Soil
1. **Recognizing Cause and Effect:** Dryland farming allows ground left fallow to replenish the nutrients necessary for crops to grow and thrive. It also conserves groundwater.
2. **Extrapolating Data/Information:** In the United States, areas in the Midwest, the northern and southern Plains, and the corn belt are possible answers.

## Activity 7 _____ page 7
### Buffering Against Erosion
1. **Comparing and Contrasting:** Wetlands, grass buffers, and forest buffers all filter sediment and chemicals from runoff resulting from rainfall. Wetlands and some forest buffers occur naturally, but grass pathways and hedges and other forest buffers are planted. Grass buffers and zone two of planted forest buffers can be harvested.
2. **Making Judgments:** Rain is not the only cause of erosion. The Dust Bowl eroded during a drought, due to wind and poor farming methods. Also, farmers need to control the amount of chemicals that flow into surface and groundwater with farming techniques in addition to buffers.
3. **Making Predictions or Interpretations:** Some runoff ends up in groundwater, which ends up, in many cases, as drinking water, and in other cases as water for crop irrigation. High levels of some chemicals in drinking or irrigation water can be harmful to the humans or livestock that drink this water and eat these crops. Other runoff ends up in surface water—streams,

rivers, lakes, and the ocean. Chemicals in this water can affect fish that humans eat as well as other animals in the water ecosytems.

## Activity 8 _____ page 8
### Life on Mars?
1. **Drawing Conclusions:** Ocean bottoms are generally smooth because of sediment depositing on the seafloor.
2. **Recognizing Cause and Effect:** Water is necessary for life, and oceans might have been the first environments to contain life on Earth.
3. **Extrapolating Data/Information:** There should be volcanoes and evidence of earthquakes, as well as mountains.
4. **Making Predictions or Interpretations:** There should be age evidence, older rock existing farther from the fissure point, and the movement of plates that could be measured.
5. **Making a Hypothesis:** Students' answers will vary but will likely suggest finding other areas in which the two planets—Earth and Mars—can be compared.

## Activity 9 _____ page 9
### Detecting Earthquake Patterns
1. **Making Judgments:** Students' answers will vary. Some students might say that strange animal behavior frequently has been observed before earthquakes occur and could signal other earthquakes. Other students might suggest that animal behavior is not a reliable predictor of earthquakes. Animal behavior could go unobserved or be related to something other than earthquakes.
2. **Making Predictions:** Students might note that the types of information now available to researchers and the continued work of scientists could lead to accurate short-term predictions in the future.
3. **Developing a Perspective:** Students' answers will vary. Some students might conclude that prediction research is a valid effort that could save lives and, therefore, should be funded. Others might think that the money could be better used for other projects, such as medical research or social programs.

# Answer Key (continued)

## Activity 10 _____ page 10
### Energy from Earth

1. **Evaluating Information:** Hot springs form where there's a lot of groundwater. Mud pots form where there's some water but not enough to settle the mud. Fumaroles form where there's just enough water to turn into steam, which forces out gases.

2. **Comparing and Contrasting:** Students' answers will vary but should include some discussion of environmental issues, such as air pollution caused by the burning of coal and land contamination possibly caused by the storage of nuclear waste. They also might discuss the relative costs of the three types of power; hydrothermal and nuclear energies are renewable and basically free, once the potentially expensive power plants are built. Coal is not renewable and therefore could become more and more expensive, but it would cost less to keep existing coal power plants than to build new nuclear or hydrothermal plants.

## Activity 11 _____ page 11
### Xenotime Dating

1. **Extrapolating Data/Information:** Xenotime dating measures the amount of lead in a sample of rock. If lead were to move from one sample of rock to another, xenotime dating would not be accurate, because a sample would appear older than it is.

2. **Making Predictions or Interpretations:** The top layer of rock with a higher lead measurement of 27 is older than the bottom layer because the uranium in the xenotime in the rock has had more time to decay, forming more lead than the bottom layer. Although you might suspect the older rock to be beneath the younger rock, tectonic forces in this case must have forced the older layer above the younger one.

3. **Classifying:** In order, the Precambrian era, the Paleozoic era, the Mesozoic era, and the Cenozoic era would have decreasing levels of lead in xenotime. The older a rock is, the larger the amount of lead in the xenotime within it.

## Activity 12 _____ page 12
### Birds and Dinosaurs—Related or Not?

1. **Classifying:** Students' answers will vary but should show logical reasoning and be supported by facts. Students might choose some of the following criteria as a basis for classifying an animal as a bird: having wings, having a bone structure suitable for flight, being warm-blooded, or other traits common to birds.

2. **Evaluating Information:** Students' answers will vary but should show logical reasoning. Sample answer: The fact that *Microraptor* was about the size of a crow, had bones similar in structure to bird bones, and had feathers and toes like birds means that it probably was an ancestor to modern birds. Added to that, the fact that it had many dinosaurlike traits, such as the tail and teeth, means that it probably was a dinosaur. Therefore, birds and dinosaurs are closely related. The fact the *Microraptor* had feathers even though it could not fly indicates that the feathers served another purpose than flight. If the feathers were for insulation, then *Microraptor,* and at least some dinosaurs, were warm-blooded. Finally, the fact that *Microraptor* had toes that could have grasped tree branches means that birds probably learned to fly from trees down.

## Activity 13 _____ page 13
### Keeping the Atmosphere Healthy

1. **Examining and Evaluating Assumptions:** Students' answers will vary. Some might agree that because industrialized nations produce more CFCs than less industrialized nations, cutting down on the amount that they produce will have a greater impact on the ozone layer. Cutting down on the amount of CFCs that less-developed countries use will have much less of an effect. Others might say that any amount of CFCs produced reduces the ozone layer, so all countries should limit production.

2. **Assessing Solutions:** Students' answers will vary. Besides the issue of avoiding CFCs, you would have to consider other environmental factors, such as energy efficiency and fuel usage, as well as possible pollution generation. You would need to think about trade-offs: is

26

your idea going to avoid one problem and create others? You don't want to leave a problem for future generations to solve. Other considerations include cost, space limitations, ease of maintenance, and cooling capability.

## Activity 14 _____ page 14
### Snowball Earth
1. **Making a Hypothesis:** If moisture from the oceans were trapped under huge sheets of ice, no water could have evaporated into the air to absorb the carbon dioxide emitted by the volcanoes. Carbon dioxide would have built up, raising Earth's temperatures and melting the ice. As the ice melted, the Sun's light would not be reflected back into the atmosphere as much as before, raising temperatures more and melting more ice. Water vapor, now able to be released into the air, would also raise temperatures, increasing the rate at which the ice would melt.
2. **Extrapolating Data/Information:** Because new pavement has a much lower albedo than dry desert, new pavement would reflect less of the Sun's radiation, absorbing it instead. This would increase the surface temperature.

## Activity 15 _____ page 15
### The Ocean—An Abundant Source of Salt
1. **Clarifying Issues:** There are many different processes for the desalination of ocean water because no one process is perfect. Scientists are looking for a process that works and that's not too expensive.
2. **Making Predictions:** The need for desalination probably will increase as populations increase, desertification in some areas continues, and commercial needs for pure water increase.

## Activity 16 _____ page 16
### The Mysterious Eel
1. **Distinguishing Relevant from Irrelevant Facts:** Answers will vary. Students might cite Schmidt's discovery of a baby eel or any other reasonable response.
2. **Drawing Conclusions:** Because parts of these life cycles are mysteries, the animals might depend upon a habitat that scientists might not be aware of. The destruction of the habitat could destroy one or more species.

## Activity 17 _____ page 17
### Plant-Based Fuels
1. **Observing and Inferring:** Students' answers will vary but might include fear of change, not wanting land to be converted from food production, worries about the expense of the conversion, worries about possible problems with the new technology, and either lack of knowledge about depleting natural resources or disbelief that resources are limited.
2. **Recognizing Cause and Effect:** Students' answers will vary but students in favor might include the following points: renewable agricultural products are good because they do not deplete the supply of fossil fuels; they do not pollute as much as gasoline or diesel; and they provide another agricultural market. Students not in favor might cite some of the same reasons as stated in the answer to question 1.

## Activity 18 _____ page 18
### Efforts to Neutralize Acid Precipitation
1. **Observing and Inferring:** The hypothesis was that adding limestone would neutralize the lake's acidity.
2. **Developing a Perspective:** Students' answers will vary. Some students might think that it is unfair to cause greater pollution problems in areas that cannot afford to meet their goals and that pollution must be controlled regardless of cost. Other students might believe that any program to reduce pollution is worthwhile.
3. **Evaluating Information:** Students' answers will vary. Students might note that it is hard to tell whether the program is working if the environment takes a long time to show an improvement. The same could be said for human health concerns. Students also might note that there are many things to judge: environmental health, human health, damage to buildings, air pollution, and cost savings.

## Activity 19 _____ page 19
### The Pros and Cons of Gene Modification
1. **Clarifying Issues:** Known problems with chemical pesticides include water and soil pollution and their possible cancer-causing properties.

2. **Observing and Inferring:** Some scientists anticipate that the newly engineered organisms could increase in number if unchecked and uncontrolled.

3. **Drawing Conclusions:** Some people will prefer the unknown—genetically modified—hoping that it's an improvement. Others will prefer the known danger—chemical—until more research is done.

4. **Developing a Perspective:** Students' answers will vary, but because the release of one organism could have an uncontrolled chain reaction, some regulation seems to be needed.

## Activity 20 _____ page 20
### Controlling the Zebra Mussel

1. **Comparing and Contrasting:** Removing the mussels by hand is safe but time-consuming and would therefore cost a great deal. Hot steam is effective and safe but doesn't solve the main problem. Chlorination is effective and safe if carefully controlled. Excessive chlorination could harm drinking water. More testing will need to be performed to determine whether potassium, bromine, ozone, and ultraviolet light are feasible alternatives. Introducing exotic predators could remove zebra mussels but might introduce more problems. Utilizing naturally occurring fish is more sensible. Trying to regulate spawning would slow growth but might introduce chemicals that could cause other problems.

2. **Assessing Solutions:** Students' answers will vary. A possible solution is to increase the cost of water for consumers. Another possible solution is government assistance.

## Activity 21 _____ page 21
### Recycling in Space

1. **Comparing and Contrasting:** On Earth, water is purified when it flows through soil and when it evaporates and condenses. On the ISS, machines filter water in a three-step filtering process. The process on Earth takes place naturally and over some time. Astronauts can more closely monitor the machine filtering process. Machines can be fixed, but microbes could die or grow out of control.

2. **Observing and Inferring:** Plants take up space. The number of plants needed to create enough oxygen to sustain an entire flight crew over time would probably take up more room than a machine and operate more slowly. Also, plants must be watered, fed, and otherwise cared for. This would be time-consuming.

## Activity 22 _____ page 22
### Fighting Off the Winter Blues

1. **Recognizing Cause and Effect:** In higher latitudes, the number of daylight hours during winter is less than the number in the lower latitudes. As a result, people are exposed to lower light levels. SAD patients would be affected.

2. **Generating Solutions:** The number of hours during which the patient is exposed to the light could be reduced. This might reduce the side effects.

## Activity 23 _____ page 23
### Early Skywatchers

1. **Comparing and Contrasting:** The monuments were all made by early people in the Americas, and all have some connection to astronomical events.

2. **Distinguishing Relevant from Irrelevant Facts:** Students' answers will vary. Students should point out the accuracy with which the builders and painters recorded the alignments of solstices, equinoxes, and supernovas. Measurements were so exact that features still align with astronomical events after centuries have passed.

3. **Drawing Conclusions:** Students' answers will vary. Students should point out that astronomy influenced religion, festivals, and how cities were built, and therefore reveals much about the lives of early people. Scientists also might be able to identify changes that occurred in the solar system since that period.